Sugared and Spiced

100 Monologues for Girls

Mary Depner

Jelliroll, Inc.

www.Jelliroll.com

Sugared and Spiced
100 Monologues for Girls

A Jelliroll Book
Published by Jelliroll, Inc
Fort Lauderdale, Florida
www.jelliroll.com

ISBN 978-1-4243-4415-4

Sugared and Spiced

100 Monologues for Girls

Mary Depner

Jelliroll, Inc.

www.Jelliroll.com

This book is dedicated to all of my former Drama students at Nova Middle School and Parkway School of the Arts.

Foreword

To the actress who chooses to perform one or many of the Sugared and Spiced monologues:

I would like to challenge you to make each monologue your own. You can do this by giving your character a pre-life. Decide upon what has taken place in this character's life up to the very minute that your monologue begins. Your decision, your character's pre-life story, will be different than any other actress's pre-life story. This will make your monologue unique.

My advice is that you don't share the pre-life story you create with anyone else. It will be your secret; the secret that will give your character her life. The only way that you should communicate this pre-life is in the way you perform your monologue.

Cover Design: Stefan Depner

Table of Contents

Table of Contents

Table of Contents

Table of Contents

First Date

Can I tell you about my first date?
Well, I haven't really had one.
Don't laugh, it's true.
Hey, I'm only 13.
I mean, it's not that I haven't been asked.
I have.
By Thomas Ryerson.
Shut up!
He's cute and you know it.
Okay, maybe he isn't a movie star.
Neither am I.
Or you, for that matter.
So, I wouldn't talk.
Besides, he's sweet.
I like him.
I HAD TO SAY NO!
Because I'm only 13 and my parents won't let me go
on a date until I'm 16 years old.
So, maybe when I'm 16, Thomas Ryerson and I will go out.
If he still likes me.
Do you think he will?

Oops!

(typing on the keyboard and speaking aloud)
Dear Robert, colon,
I love you sooooo much. (giggle)
The moment I saw you in Mrs. Herbert's Science classI...
(stops to think)
Hmm... I...
I just about fainted.
Your soft wavy brown hair.
Those amazing blue eyes.
The way you chew your gum.
(sigh)
If only you were mine.
I would be the happiest girl in the whole world!
I love you, I love you, I lo..
(sharply turns to the right)
WHAT MOM?
Oh, did I lock the door? Sorry! Just a second, let me save this email I was writing.
(clicks quickly)
Oh! Oh NOOOO!
(reading screen)
Your email has been sent to Robert@ ...
(voice trails off, then hysterically)
I want my email back!!!

Old Friends

(Waves cheerily) Hi Denise! How's it going?

(Aside to Camille) Oh my gosh, can you believe that outfit she's wearing?
I mean it's the first day of school, not prom night!
(Snickering) And we used to be such good friends! What was I thinking?

(Waves again) Hey Donny! What's goin on?
(Aside to Camille) What a nerd. Oh my gosh! And he acts like he's in love with me.
Did you catch how he practically stopped breathing when I said "hello".
(laughing) Dude! Get a life!

(To Camille) Hey, where are you going?
(with an attitude) Excuse me?
Me? Rude?
How can you say that about me?
Hunh!
(stands alone looking upset)
And we used to be such good friends.

First Kiss

My first kiss was on the school bus with Danny Black.
I was in seventh grade and he kissed me right on the lips just as I got on the bus.
Oh yeah, right there in front of the bus with everyone watching.
It was Christmas time and he had a sprig of mistletoe that he wanted to put to good use.
Well...he sure did. He planted a kiss on me and the whole bus practically exploded with laughter. I could have died.
And I've never spoken to him again.
But you know what?
It was kind of nice.
The kiss, I mean.
It was all soft and warm.
And he tasted like strawberry bubble gum.
I'll never tell that to him.
Not in a million years!
It will go with me all the way to the grave.
But, I do have a new favorite flavor of bubble gum now.
Strawberry.

I'd Rather Be...

My dad has a bumper sticker that says
"I'd rather be sailing."
You know, the funny thing is that he doesn't even know how to sail.
He's never even been. Never really wants to go.
He told me that the bumper sticker really just means that he'd rather be doing anything else in this world rather than what he does.
He drives all day, delivering hardware for Moe and Son's Hardware.
He hates traffic.
He hates driving.
And, I think he hates hardware.

I wonder, when I grow up, will I have a job that I hate too?
Sometimes, when I'm in school, I'd rather be sailing.
But not most days.
Most days...I'd just rather be at the mall.

First Fight

Dad and I had our first fight.
I know it's hard to believe. I've lived with the man for over 12 years and we never ever had a fight until yesterday.
And I think that I cried the entire night last night.
I think that yesterday was probably the worst day of my life.
You see, I said things that I really didn't mean, but...
I was so angry. I wanted to make him feel as bad as I did.
And...unfortunately, I did.
I wish I could go back a day and make everything okay again.
I hope he forgives me.
I know one thing, if he does, I promise, I swear, that I will never, ever fight with him again.

Under Where?

You hid my shoes under where?
Under that old stinky mattress in the basement?
Are you insane?
Those shoes cost me my entire summer camp counselor wages last year, nitwit!
No duh! They are VERY expensive.
That's why I had to buy them myself.
That's why mom wouldn't buy them for me!
That's why I GOT A JOB IN THE FIRST PLACE!
Go get them. RIGHT NOW!
Clean them off and NEVER, EVER, EVER touch them again.
If there is one scratch on them, your piggy bank is MINE!

Tooth Decay

I haven't brushed my teeth in a month!
I'm on strike.
Yep, that's right.
On strike.
Also, you may have noticed that I haven't washed my hair.
Nope. Not once. Not once this entire month.
That's right!
On strike there too.
And yep! You guessed it.
These jeans...haven't washed them in a month and I've worn them every single day. Sometimes to bed at night too.
And you know what? I think it's working.
I think Mr. Williams is finally going to give in and move me to the back of the room.
Well, I hope he does it soon.
I think I'm getting a cavity.

My Lips are Sealed

I can't believe what I just saw.
Penelope Constanza Moriarity kissing Edward Pierson behind the gym. He is in high school. He is in ninth grade.
She is not allowed to even date boys yet.
Let alone kiss them behind the gym!
I could get her in sooo much trouble.
If I told her mother, she would be ...
Well, probably grounded for life.
Her father just happens to be the principal of Dewbury Middle.
The "finest institution of academia in the South".
She is sooo lucky that I'm not a snitch.
My lips are sealed.
You won't tell, will you?

Grasshopper

I have this secret fantasy that I'm a grasshopper.
I know it's strange, but it started when I was in fifth grade.
My big brother Harry had to collect bugs for an insect collection for his Advanced Biology class for super nerds.
Well, anyway, the first bug he caught was a grasshopper.
It looked so sad and forlorn all pinned down in that shoe box.
That night I had a dream.
I dreamed that the grasshopper escaped and he and I were hopping through a beautiful field of flowers.
He told me that his name was Jim and that I was the most beautiful grasshopper he had ever seen.
So, every now and then, when I'm a little bored and lonely, I'll dream a little dream.
And I'm a grasshopper once more.
(hops off stage)

Things that Make Me Really Mad

You know what makes me really mad?
People who don't know how to wait in line.
I mean, you go to the mall and get in line to buy a hot dog, let's say.
There's one person in front of you, but that one person in front of you somehow multiplies into three people.
Cause her two friends just kind of giggle their way into line right next to her and pretend that you don't even exist.

Hey, are you even listening?
(shaking her head)
Another thing that makes me really mad!
(storms off)

First Love

Excuse me if I'm a little....strange.
You see, I haven't been the same since last night.
Last night I met someone and I think this is it.
I'm in love.
I think.
I'm not sure, because it's never happened before.
But, I sure do feel strange. Kind of...awake, but still dreaming.
Kind of walking on a cloud I guess.
Couldn't eat breakfast.
Didn't make the bus.
Found myself smiling all the way to school.
Guess this is it.
Wow!
First love.

No Juice for You

When I was in Kindergarten we used to get juice and an oatmeal cookie every day after naptime.
One day at naptime, I couldn't sleep.
So, I ended up talking the entire time to this cute little boy lying on the mat next to mine.
When naptime was over, Mrs. Bell called us all to get in line for our cookie and juice, as usual.
I waited in line, but when it was my turn she just looked at me and said, "You don't get a cookie and juice today, Miss Mary. You talked during naptime."
To do this day I don't talk a lot in school. I'm always the "quiet one". I guess that's okay, but I think that might have traumatized me a little bit. The whole juice and cookie thing.
At least my mother says so. She's always telling me to come out of my shell.
Oh well, I guess Mrs. Bell thought she was doing the right thing.
She just wanted to teach me a lesson. That's all.

Ice Cream Sunday

When I lived with my mom, we used to go for a Sundae every Sunday. It's funny, but I always thought that every kid did that. She would go around the house singing "A Sundae on a Sunday" and my brother and I would run to put on our sneakers, or our sweaters and coats.
In the summer, I would look for my flip-flops that were usually hiding under the bed. Funny, but I thought those sundaes were the best sundaes in the world. And I thought those Sundays would never end. But they did.
I don't live with my mom anymore and Sunday is just like any other day.
And whenever I'm eating a sundae, with caramel or strawberry topping, those were her favorites....I always think of her.

Chinese Take Out

I love food from all over the world.
My dad is German and he makes the most amazing red cabbage.
Usually on Tuesdays.
Mom is from Cuba and her black beans and rice are the best in the universe. She makes them a lot. We have black beans and rice with chicken. Black beans and rice with lamb chops, and black beans and rice with hamburgers too.
But on Fridays...Friday nights are different.
We all get in the car and drive over to "the best little Chinese Take Out spot in this hemisphere". At least that's what dad always calls it.
We order Sweet and Sour Chicken, Fried Rice, and Egg Rolls.
We take it home and get out the chopsticks and you know what, we always eat every bite.
Not a crumb left for a mouse. If we had mice that is.
Hmm. I guess you might say that every week for me is like a little culinary trip around the world.

The Audition

My palms are sweating!
How gross!
I've always heard adults say that their palms got sweaty when they were nervous, but I couldn't relate.
And now, it's happening to me!!
Yuck!
(talking to self) It's only an audition. Stay calm!
It is just the school play.
It's not Broadway for crying out loud.
It's not the movies.
I am not going to make or break my acting career with a part in Ms. Calhoun's production of "The Hog and the Ham."
But I want this sooo bad!
I would make such a cute hen.
I've been practicing walking up and down pecking for food.
Talking in my best hen's voice.
(hears something)
Oh, my gosh, that's me.
I'm on!!!
Wish me luck!
Oops! I mean tell me to break a leg!
Or a drumstick.
(Walks off cackling like a hen)

Me, a Cheerleader?

(in the middle of a cheer)
Fight, Fight, Fight with all your might!
GOOO RAIDERS!!

Well, I think that was pretty good.
Tomorrow is the final cut, so I'll find out then if I made the squad.
Hmmm.
Me, a cheerleader?
I just don't see it.
But, mom says you have to visualize what you want, so I'm trying.
(closes her eyes)
Let's see. I'm walking down the hall in my cute little orange and white uniform with a big fuzzy N on the sweater.
(opens her eyes and continues the fantasy)
The other cheerleaders wait for me by the lockers. Buffy, Huffy, and Hanna.
We're all going over to Buffy's house to brush our hair and put on fresh lip gloss.
Danny Zobie, the absolute cutist guy in the 8th grade, stops me in the hall and asks me to the Spring Dance.
"Me Danny? Sure, I'd love to go with you."

(back to reality)
Hmmm. Maybe I'd better practice one more time.
Fight team, fight!!

Why Me?

Why am I always the one who sits alone at lunch?
Why can't I meet someone who likes me just the way I am?
Who likes my company?
It's always me alone at lunch, in a new school, in a new city.
My sister Sarah meets new people and instantly they're best friends forever. She's over there at that picnic table right now with a bunch of the most popular kids in the school.
It just doesn't work for me.
I look just like Sarah, but I'm different.
Personality-wise.
I'm quiet and everyone says I'm shy.
I hate that word.
Sarah...she's outgoing and funny.
"Gregarious", my English teacher said.
I like to read and watch old movies on TV.
Sarah's athletic, and is usually the best at everything.
Why can't I be the popular one?

The Worst Possible Day

I got it. Yippee.
It's here and it's the worst possible day.
Yep, that's right.
I finally got my period.
For three years I kept wondering, "Why don't I ever get it, the curse, my cousin Nancy, whatever the heck you want to call it? What's wrong with me?"
Well, I mean, I used to think, I'm fourteen years old and I'm as much of a woman as Theresa Lindy is. She got hers when she was only eleven, or twelve I think.
So, now, lucky me, I've joined the club.
On the worst possible day.
The State Champion swim meet.
Yippee.
Oh well, the joys of being a girl.

Crazy Armpits

My armpits are crazy.
They talk to me when no one else is around.
I'd show you, but they know you're here so they won't do it.
Hey, wait a second. (Covers her armpits with her hands and whispers) Go over there and hide behind that tree and I'll act like I'm all alone. Go on. (walks around whistling like she's all alone. Then, glances slyly over to the tree.)
I can see your feet! Can't you hide better than that?!
Me? Crazy?
I'm crazy?
I just told you!
It's not me, it's them!
Of course you didn't hear anything.
They knew you were here all the time.
(Shouts after her)
Fine! Go ahead and leave.
(Sits down, disgusted.)
(Then looks down at her armpits)
Oh, shut up!

Fernsnickel Hooves

My name is Fernsnickle Hooves.
That's okay, go ahead and laugh.
My parents gave me that name just so that everyone would laugh at me.
They wanted me to build character.
They wanted me to be "ready to take on the world".
Well, they were right. I guess.
I am a very capable and thick-skinned young woman, with a lot of character and a good head on my shoulders.
On the other hand, however, it has been a bit difficult.
Being taken seriously, that is.
Like in the first grade, when I walked into class and the teacher asked innocently, "What's your name dear?" I said "Fernsickle Hooves" and the entire class was rolling on the floor.
Needless to say, I had to stand in the corner for an entire day.
Well, one day, I'm going to get married and I'll be Fernsnickle Smith or Fernsnickle Johnson and maybe I'll get a little more respect.
And maybe, one day, I'll even shorten my first name so it's a little less hilarious.
I think Snickle would be nice, don't you?

Pink Lemonade

Last year I went for a long walk on the hottest day of the year.
I didn't know it was the hottest day until I got about two miles from home.
At that point the sun was beating down on me so hot that I started to imagine that a tall glass of Pink Lemonade was just a few feet in front of me. Kind of like a mirage.
Every time I felt it within my grasp, it dissolved.
It was very perplexing, I might add.
It just disintegrated into a steamy vapor.
Mmmmm. Cool icy Pink Lemonade, melted by the sun.
If you'll excuse me, I'm getting just a bit thirsty.

Ticklish

I'm ticklish and it's a real problem.
Oh yeah, yeah, I know. You're ticklish too.
Everybody's ticklish.
But (laughs unexpectedly) nobody is ticklish like I'm ticklish.
(Laughs as if she's being tickled on her side)
As you can see, I'm ticklish even when I'm not actually being tickled. It's a rare condition and it's quite em (almost can't finish the word for her giggling) embarrassing.
Pardon me, but it's a little worse than usual today.
I think it gets worse when I'm nervous and doing this monologue (giggles and wiggles and bends) has made me so nervous that (giggling uncontrollably) I'd better let it come to an end.

Fudge Puppy

My new puppy is teaching me to bark.
See, I'll show you.
(Calling the puppy) Here Cee Cee.
CEEEE CEEEE
That's a good girl. Come to mama.
She thinks I'm her mother.
Now, Cee Cee, show the nice people how you're teaching me to bark. Teaching me to be a puppy just like you.
(Mimes petting the dog.)
Yeah, good girl. Now, go ahead, show me how to bark.
(Listens to Cee Cee barking and then replies)
Ruff, Ruff. Grrrrrr. Ruff, Grrruff, Grrrrr
(looks at audience)
Pretty good, eh?
(To Cee Cee)
What's that Cee Cee? I did a good job? Oh goooodie!!
Thank you Cee Cee.
(Reaches over and mimes taking a piece of fudge out of a jar and puts it in her mouth.)
(Talking with her mouth full) Mmmm, delicious.
See, everytime I do a good job, she lets me have a piece of fudge.
She calls me her fudge puppy.

Michael's Wish

My brother Michael is my best friend.
He's sick a lot and has to spend a lot of time away from home, in the hospital.
Mom and Dad and I try to be there for him as much as we can, but it's really hard. We've had a lot of medical bills and my mom has to work two jobs.
My dad had to take a better paying job which makes him travel a lot. So he's probably gone about 75 percent of the month these days.
You know, it's really made me realize how important our family time together is.
And that's what Michael wishes.
That one day, we'll be just like any normal family that comes home at night to be together.
It seems like a simple thing to most people.
But for us, right now...
It's only a dream.

Jealousy

They say that jealousy is a Green-Eyed Monster.
I actually painted a picture of her last year in art class.
All grey and brown with warts.
Eyes that were huge and just popping out of her head.
Bright green glowing eyes, like they are on fire.
It's funny, but I recognized myself in that picture.
I decided to hang it in my bedroom and on days when I can't stand to see anyone have anything that I want...
I call it my Self Portrait.

The Break Up

Mikey, we need to talk.
Nothing's wrong, well sort of.
There's just..
Something that I need to tell you.
I can't go out with you anymore.
(sigh of relief)
There, I said it.
Oh, don't cry, please.
Please, please, please, don't cry.
Wow, I've never seen you shed one tear before.
I didn't mean to hurt you.
It's not that bad, really it's not.
You're only 13.
You'll meet a million other girls in your lifetime that you love.
(Searching for the right words.)
It couldn't go on forever, you know.
And it's not because I don't like you.
I'm just really into school.
And my friends.
I'm sorry Mikey, but I just can't do the relationship thing right now.

Wedding Bells

My dad is getting remarried tomorrow.
I'm sure I've said enough right there to give you some idea of how complex my life is at the moment.
In short, it's VERY COMPLEX.
Oh, it's not like my new stepmother is not nice.
She is.
Right now.
But, what will she be like when she is actually my dad's WIFE?
I'm not sure.
I've heard a lot of horror stories you know.
Like *Cinderella,* for instance.
And then there's my mom. She's acting like she's 100 percent okay with this. Just fine and dandy.
But....I have this weird feeling that she is going to freak tomorrow, when she has to drop me off at the church.
The SAME church that she and my dad were married in about 20 years ago!
I think she's going to freak.
And then what will I do?
Why can't my life just be a little bit easier?

Kristy Lynn

I'm babysitting tonight!
I'm sooo excited.
Ever since our new neighbors moved in, I've been babysitting a few times a month and I LOVE IT!
Kristy Lynn is the cutest, most adorable baby in the world.
And she loves me for some crazy reason.
It's funny, but one time, they decided to let her grandmother watch her instead of me, and sure enough around 8:30 at night she came knocking on my door.
"Can Amy please come over? Kristy Lynn is crying and she won't go to bed. She wants Amy to come over."
What can I say?
I'm just a natural with little kids.

Step Dad

It's strange, but my step dad is really like, well, just plain dad to me.
When he came into my life, I was a little worried.
Everything he said seemed foreign to me. Like he was speaking another language, you know.
But, now, it's been two years, and I have to say that he's really turned out okay.
More than okay.
Great actually.
Sometimes I catch myself calling him Dad instead of Stephen and it feels just fine.
I never thought I'd see that day.
I guess it's just because of the way he treats me.
The way he has treated mom and me from the day he moved into the house.
Well, he's really not just a step dad anymore.
He's a part of our family.

The Funeral

The only funeral that I've ever been to was for my grandfather.
It was terrible because we all loved him so much.
And it was terrible because you're in pain and crying and on top of that all of the people that you love are in pain and crying too.
So, you feel bad for yourself and for everyone else.
I felt really bad for my mom.
And my grandmother, too.
My granddad was her whole life. They were married for about 50 years. Can you imagine that? That's like my entire lifetime four times over.
I never want to go to another funeral again.
But, I never want to forget this one either.
I think it really helped me to understand just how important it is to let go of anger and resentment over little things.
Especially with the people you love.
Cause they won't be here forever.

The Mighty Five

My cousins and my brother and I are going to open a restaurant called The Mighty Five.
We're going to serve hamburgers and fries and all that good stuff.
We're all going to wait tables and do the cooking.
It's called The Mighty Five because there are five of us.
Lynnie, Bobby, Tammy, Sammy and me.
This is our plan, anyway.
I'm not sure how we'll do it, but I've been practicing for the day that our dream becomes a reality.
(Pretends to wait on a table)
Excuse me sir, would you like another glass of tea?
(To another table)
Pardon me ma'm? Oh, certainly, I'll bring that right away.
(to the audience)
You see I'm a natural.
(Starts to leave and then turns quickly to the last table)
Oh, would you like fries with that?

He Drinks Too Much

My mom is dating a guy who drinks too much.
It worries me because she really, really likes him a lot.
I mean, I like him too, but he drinks too much.
And it's not like it's cool or funny or anything you see in the movies.
It's like he's two different people and you never know who you're going to get.
I don't like it when he hangs out at our house on the weekends.
Lately, I try to stay over with a friend as much as I can.
The other day, mom asked me, "What do you think about Don? Cause I really like him a lot you know."
I wanted to shout ARE YOU BLIND???...THE MAN DRINKS WAAAAY TOO MUCH!!!
Instead I just said, " Yeah, mom, he's cool."
She just smiled and tapped me on the head.

Daisy

My best friend in the world is named Daisy.
She's my dog of course.
A German Shepard Doberman Pincher mix.
We got her at the pound.
She sounds like she'd be ferocious, I know, but she's really as sweet as sugar, that dog.
She loves to run in the yard and go for rides in the car.
She hates to get a bath and shakes and shivers until it's all over.
Sometimes, when I'm having a particularly bad day at school, I just remember that she's at home waiting for me and a smile immediately comes on my face.
As soon as I get home from school, I take her for a walk and tell her everything. She's the only friend I have that can keep a secret.

Buster

Buster the kitty cat came into my life when I was only nine.
He's black and fuzzy and round.
Well, I guess you'd actually say that he's fat for a cat.
He came to our house as a stray and at first we didn't want him to stay.
Mom said, "Don't feed him, because then he'll be here forever."
But he was so persistent.
He just kept hanging around and finally we couldn't resist.
He has these funny teeth that are like crooked fangs and when he's sleeping he stretches out on his back with his mouth open and snores. Then at times, he gets this smile on his face like he's having a really good dream.
Dreaming of whatever cats dream of I guess.
A rat, a mouse??
Buster...
He's the best thing that ever happened to me.

Myrtle the Turtle

When my grandmother was a little girl, kids used to call her
Myrtle the Turtle and she hated it.
Myrtle is actually a pretty name because it's the name of a
plant.
But, some people think it sounds funny, so I guess they thought
they could hurt her feelings by calling her that.
My grandmother is a really strong person though.
She would never really let anything that anyone says bother
her. And I have to say that I totally admire her for that.
In fact, she's probably the strongest person I know.
Which is good, because hopefully I've inherited a little of that.
Whenever I'm feeling down I try to remind myself that
somewhere inside of me is a little bit of my grandmother.
Myrtle the Beautiful Turtle.

The Dance

I don't like to brag, but...whenever there's an argument, or a problem to solve, I'm always right.
And...even though I usually come up with the right solution to every problem, I generally get ignored anyway.
Everyone acts like "How could a twelve year old girl possibly know what she's talking about?"
So, I go ahead and tell them what I think and then I just smile as they ignore me and listen to someone else who they think is soooo much older and wiser.
And then I just wait.
Patiently.
And sure enough,
I'm always right.
And that's when, my friends, I break into my beautiful
I TOLD YOU SO dance.
It goes like this...
(dancing off the stage and singing)
I told you so, I told you so, I told you soooo.

Before

(Throughout this entire monologue, she is looking in the mirror, putting on makeup and jewelry and brushing her hair.)

I have a date tonight with the hottest, most popular guy in our school. David Perry.
All of the girls in my class love him.
So...I was pretty happy when he called on Thursday to ask me out.
I'm not the most popular girl in the school,
But...I'm pretty popular.
And this...will make me even more popular.
(Dreamily) A date with David Perry.
Plus, I think it will be fun.
He has a really cool car and I like the way he dresses.
That's why I have to look my absolute best.
I bought a new outfit, new earrings, and new makeup.
How do I look?

After

(Throughout the entire monologue, she taking off her jewelry, brushing her teeth, taking off makeup, and getting ready for bed.
Talking to herself in the mirror...)

Well, I'm home.
After what was supposed to be the biggest date of my life.
David Perry.
The most popular guy in school.
So cute, so cool, and well, honestly..
Sooo boring.
We just didn't click.
When I tried to be funny, he didn't laugh.
When he tried to be funny, he was just rude.
What a disappointment.
NOTHING IN COMMON AT ALL!
(sighs)
Oh well, love is not about popularity.
Or looks, apparently.
There has to be something more inside of a person.
Well, at least I learned that one thing is true.
You can't judge a book, or a person, by its cover.

Thirty-Two

My best friend Cecelia and I have shortened the language.
The English language that is.
We got sick of saying a lot of the same things over and over again.
Like "How's it going?" "What are you up to?" "What's on T.V. Tonight?"
And I'm sure you can think of a million others.
So, now when Cecelia and I want to say "How's it going?" we just say "32."
And, if it's going okay, we just say "48."
Not so great is "negative 8."
That one is almost as long as the original phrase, so at first we voted to kick it out of our lexicon.
But then, it just sounded so cool that we put it right back in.
I mean, why say "not so great" when you can say "negative eight"?

Yellow Ribbon

We tied a yellow ribbon on the big palm tree in front of our house yesterday.
My brother Tom is in the Air Force and he's been in Iraq for 3 months now.
I really miss him a lot and want him to come home more and more every day.
Sometimes in school I think about him and I start getting scared that I'll never see him again.
Mom is scared too.
We all are.
The day that Tom comes home is going to the best day of our lives.
We plan on having a huge party with the entire neighborhood there.
And that yellow ribbon?
That will be history.

The Silent Treatment

I just love getting the silent treatment, don't you?
I have this friend, well, ex-friend, who is giving me the silent treatment as we speak.
The worst part is, I don't even know what I did to deserve it.
We were in the cafeteria having lunch.
Everything seemed normal to me.
But when we got into chorus class, it started.
The Silent Treatment.
She would not talk to me.
I asked her what was wrong and she wouldn't answer.
You know, that's kind of immature, don't you think?
I can't even apologize for whatever I did, cause I haven't even got a clue.
When she's ready to talk, I'll listen.
But...I don't think I want to be friends anymore.

The Spelling Bee

My best friend Carol won the state spelling bee last year and
I think her head swelled to about the size of a school bus.
She came back from the competition with this whole new
attitude.
I mean, I don't want to sound like sour grapes, and I'm sure
that I probably do.
But you can really ask anybody.
She's just not the same.
We hardly ever spend time together anymore, and when we
do,
she never listens when I talk.
She just wants to talk about herself about 100 percent of the
time.
In fact, the other day at lunch, I pretended that I had to do
some homework, just so I wouldn't have to listen to her go
on and on about her latest triumph.
But she went on and on anyway.
So at one point I interrupted her and said, "Hey Carol, how
do you spell humility?"

A Magic Carpet

To me a really good book is the best present that anyone could ever give me.
When I have a really good book I can spend an entire day in my room and I never feel alone.
It's like the whole world goes away and you enter this other world of characters and events.
People and places.
Like traveling without ever
getting out of your chair.
A sort of Magic Carpet really.
When I have a really good book, I even forget to eat sometimes.
I mean, usually I'm snacking all day, but when I'm reading, I don't even think about it.
Until Mom calls me to dinner that is.
And then I usually just take the book right to the table with me.
One day, I'd like to be an author, so that I can create a wonderful book.
And then, like a magic carpet, it will take a kid just like me to a whole new world.

Adopted Child

My mother says that when you adopt a child you expand the love in your life a million times over.
I'm her adopted child, so she's really talking about me.
My mother says that when I came into her life she was given a gift.
She was given the opportunity to share her life with me and to know what a unique and special person I am.
She says that when she brought me home as a baby, she just kept wondering silly things, like what would be my favorite flavor of ice cream, or what my favorite color would be.
She says I'm like a good book that keeps on going.
Every day we turn a new page.
And every day we have a little Strawberry Ice-Cream, my favorite, with a little Butter Pecan, that's hers.

Madam President

One day, I want to be the President of the United States.
I want to sit in the Oval Office and know what it's like to be the Commander-in-Chief.
I'm serious.
Really.
This is not something that I take lightly.
And, I've done a lot of reading and I know that every day I'm laying the foundation for my future.
So, if that's what I really want – and it is – I need to start working toward it now.
I need to learn as much as I can about history and the world.
And current events too!
A good president has to know what's happening in the world.
And I want to prove that I have a real desire to help people, because I do.
I volunteer for good causes whenever I can and I try not to do anything too stupid that will make me look like a fool.
I have to work really hard if I want to one day hear those words,
"Madam President."

The Rules of the Game

I wish people would respect the rules of life as much as they respect the rules of a game, like football for instance.
I mean, in football, if you want to win, you play by the rules.
Or you're penalized.
In life, it's that way too, but there are some rules that people think they can ignore.
Like the one that says you should treat other people the way you want to be treated.
Can you imagine what the world would be like if everybody really followed that rule?
Just take a minute to think about it.
The world would be a better place.
There wouldn't be war, or even a reason to go to war.
And, it could all start right here in this room.
Come on people, let's respect the rule and see if we can change the world.
Cause this really isn't a game.

The Cutest Couple I Know

My parents are the cutest couple that I know.
They met when they were in high school and they still act like they met just yesterday.
Always holding hands.
Whispering and giggling in the movies.
In fact, the last time they took me and my friends to the movies the people behind us had to tell them to shush.
It's kind of embarrassing in a way, but it's cute too.
And it's very rare, I know.
A lot of parents bicker and complain about each other.
And these days, when you hear a parent say "your just like your father" or "your just like your mother," they don't usually mean it as a compliment.
But with my parents, whenever I do something great, my dad says, "You're just like your mom."
And when I'm super funny or cute, my mom always says, "that's so cute...just like your dad."
Kind of disgusting right?
But, until I get married, they're the cutest couple I know.

Love and Stuff

I've found the cutest way to end all of my notes and emails these days. I just sign off with "Love and Stuff."
Isn't that adorable?

I used to always end my notes with "Your Friend," or "Best Friends Forever," or the shortened version, which of course is just capital B, capital F, capital F.

Of course, the coolest way to sign off is just to say "Whatever."
Like you just don't care. And I went through that stage for a while.
Like, I sent an email to Carol Derer about my trip to Key West with my church youth group. It was actually a really cool trip, but I know everyone thinks we're a bunch of nerds. So, I just said, "Yeah, it was fun. We went kayaking and played games at night."
And then I signed off with "Whatever, Dee."

But "Love and Stuff" is so much better, don't you think?
I mean it's not for everybody. I mean, there are still a few people who might get their feelings hurt if I don't sign off with "BFF."
And sometimes, when I want to be really cool, I still say, "Whatever!"

Fifteen Minutes at the Grand Canyon

This Christmas my parents took my brother and me to Las Vegas.
It was pretty cool.
But it wasn't a normal Christmas.
You know, Las Vegas is just not your typical warm, fuzzy spot for caroling and ho, ho, ho.
But, the coolest part of the trip is that Las Vegas is really close to the Grand Canyon.
And my mother was dying to see the Grand Canyon.
So, my dad agreed to rent a car and one morning we packed up the car with snacks and water and took off for the South Rim.
There are two rims at the Grand Canyon where you can enter the park. The North Rim is really close to Las Vegas, but in the winter, it's under about ten feet of snow.
So we drove all the way to the South Rim.
And it was AMAZING.
It was freezing cold too!
We really weren't prepared for that, but because of the elevation, it was so cold that it snowed and my mom said that her fingers felt like they were frozen.
So, we only stayed about fifteen minutes, but boy it was worth the trip.
I had no idea how beautiful and awe inspiring that place could be.
You just can't capture beauty like that in a photograph.

My Wedding

When I get married, my wedding is going to be an amazing event.
It's going to be a theme wedding, just like some people have theme Bat Mizvahs.
Well, the theme of my wedding is going to be *The Wizard of Oz*.
I'm going to dress like the Good Witch and all of the guests will be asked to dress like munchkins or those monkeys that flew through the sky.
My bridesmaids will be dressed like the bad witch and the ushers and the best man will be the scare crow, the tin man and the cowardly lion.
The groom will be....
Let's see, the groom will be...
Hmmm, no I don't want him to be the man behind the curtain.
Okay, when I get married, the theme is going to be *The Lord of the Rings*...
I am going to be...
Well, I'll have to get back to you.

Surprise Party

SHHHHH! This is a SURPRISE party.
Surprise being the key word in that sentence.
Ya'll need to hush up a bit.
Okay, Billy you hide over there, and Sammy you get under the table.
The rest of you just kind of crouch down behind the couch.
Oh, my gosh, I think I hear keys in the door.
(runs and crouches down behind the couch with the others, listening intently)
(Whispers) Oh my gosh, I forgot to turn off the lights.
(Gets up and quickly does so, then hides behind the couch)
(Listens again and then whispers)
Okay ya'll, this is it. One, two, three...
(jumps up) SURPRISE!
(hops and dances and wiggles and giggles- very pleased with herself)
Surprise, surprise, surpriiiiiiise!
(Notices her guest's reaction)
What's the matter, aren't you surprised?
Well, it's your birthday today silly.
Yes it is! March 22nd. That's your birthday right?
(looks surprised) It's not?
When is it?
June 28th?
(embarrassed)
Well, gee then, I guess this really is a surprise!

Mentira

Today in Spanish class we learned a new vocabulary word.
Mentira (men – tear –ah)
Which means lie.
It was a really weird word to learn today, because just last night I lied to my mother.
Not a tiny little white lie, or a fib, but a gigantic terrible lie.
Now, I'm sorry that I did.
And I don't know what would be harder. To tell the truth and face the consequences, or to live with the guilt and the fear.
Fear that she'll find out and never trust me again.
Fear that she'll find out and be disappointed in me and hurt.
I'm starting to wonder if I should just be brave and go to her and confess. NOW before it's too late.
But I'm afraid to.
If I tell her I lied, I'll be in trouble twice.
Once for what I lied about and then even more for lying.
(Ugggh!)
Mentira! I hate that word.
I wish it wasn't part of my vocabulary in any language.

Hopscotch

(She hopscotches throughout the entire monologue without stopping)
My name is Brianna and I'm addicted to Hopscotch.
As you can see, it comes quite naturally to me.
And I do love it so.
Do I do it too much?
Maybe.
Do I care?
Noooo!
There are worse things that a person can be addicted to.
And, I don't really hopscotch all the time.
I can't do it in my sleep for instance.
I tried it once, but it didn't work.
I can't do it while I'm eating dinner either.
My mother would kill me.
I can do it while snacking though.
An apple, a popsicle. a pretzel.
There are a lot of things a girl can eat while hopping.
Of course I don't do a lot of hopping in class.
If the teacher's not looking I'll hop to the pencil sharpener, or to get a book off the shelve. That is, if there isn't some loud mouth who yells, BRIANA IS HOPPING AGAIN!
Now, out in the hallway, I hop all I want. I read the school rules and they are totally against running in the halls. But hopping? It's not mentioned at all.

Just Be Yourself

"Just be yourself."
Doesn't everyone say that when they want you to relax?
Well, for me, telling me to just be myself does not make me relax.
Actually, it sends me into a total panic.
I honestly haven't figured out who "myself" is.
I mean, I'm a lot of different things.
And, those different things change every day.
Sometimes I'm shy and sometimes I'm outgoing.
Sometimes I'm quiet and sometimes I'm loud.
When I go to a party, I never know which me is going to show up.
The one who likes to mingle or the one who can't move away from the punch bowl.
And sometimes I'm like a chameleon.
I'll change my colors to fit into whatever crowd I happen to be surrounded with.
So, telling me to be myself, for me, is like telling me to do the impossible.

Pauline the Plumber

(sitting on the floor, repairing the kitchen sink)
Okay. Just tightening her up.
(pantomiming tightening the pipes with a wrench)
Righty tighty, lefty loosey.
Okay mom, that oughta hold her for a while.
You had some really big junk stuck in there.
I know, I know I'm amazing.
Well, you taught me well. Did you time me?
Fifty minutes? Oh man!!
That's way too long. Well, let's try again next week.
Maybe if you try not to get something the size of a watermelon stuck down there it will go a little faster.

Flying Lessons

I started taking flying lessons when I was thirteen.
It's something I've dreamed about since I was a little girl.
My mom wasn't too thrilled with the idea at first.
I think it scared her a little.
But I was persistent.
I think I drove her crazy actually.
Every morning at the breakfast table, "So when do you think I'll be old enough to fly?"
Every night before I went to bed, "I hope I have another dream tonight that I can fly."
Finally, she gave in.
And you know what?
I think she's glad that she did.
Every time I take a lesson now, I'm learning a little more about flying, and she's learning a little bit more about letting go.

Smoke Signals

I caught my brother Billy smoking yesterday.
What a jerk!
I can't believe he'd be soooo stupid.
The worst thing is, I don't know what to do.
I don't think this was a one-time thing.
It looked like he's getting a lot of practice.
If my parents found out, they'd kill him.
But, if they don't find out, he'll kill himself.
By smoking.
What an idiot!
He's only fifteen.
If he starts smoking now, by the time he's twenty his lungs will probably look like that tar you step in at the beach.
What should I do?
Should I tell my parents so they can try to do something about it? I don't want to be a tattletale, but I love Billy.
If something ever happens to him, I'll just die.
And it's just peer pressure, you know.
He's not like me. I'm strong. If someone offers me a cigarette, I have no problem turning them down. I don't care who they are.
But I guess Billy had a weak moment or something.
Maybe I should talk to him first and tell him how worried I am.
I sure hope he gets the message.

Company and Fish

They say that company and fish both stink after three days and I'm beginning to understand why.
My relatives from Kansas City have been staying at our house for two weeks now.
At first I thought it was great.
I happily gave up my comfy bed and my nice private bedroom so that Uncle Harry and Aunt Regina could sleep there.
The first couple nights on the sofa bed weren't bad really.
But, now, I think I have a permanent indentation across my back from the bar that keeps poking through the mattress.
Plus, they all stay up late every night talking. Mom, Aunt Regina and Dad. Uncle Harry can't seem to keep his eyes open past eight o'clock.
Well, all that talking and reminiscing...it's keeping me up to the wee hours every morning. That's why I look like this!
Like I haven't had sleep for weeks! Cause I haven't.
It's great for mom cause she took two weeks off work.
And dad never has needed more than five hours.
But me? I'm an eight-hour a night girl.
Well, only two more days and we'll be waving goodbye.... until next year!
My Aunt Regina says she's had such a good time, that she and Uncle Harry want to do it again next Spring.
Oh yippee. Can you tell how excited I am?

Word of the Day

The word of the day is *negotiable.*
I am going to try to use that word,
negotiable, as many time as possible so that it will become an intrinsic part of my vocabulary.
Intrinsic, that was the word of the day yesterday.
The word of the day, by the way, is not negotiable.
It is handed down from the powers that be, the Seventh grade English department, Ms. Hannibal, Mr, Jordan, and Mrs. Wax.
If it were negotiable, I would argue for another word of the day like butterscotch. Butterscotch is a perfectly wonderful word and I would be forced to use it all day long if it were the word of the day.
Then when I asked my dad to take me for an ice cream sundae, it would be more negotiable because I could argue that I needed an opportunity to use the word butterscotch.
And where else would a butterscotch sundae be more negotiable than Yummy Tummy's ice cream parlor?

The Color of Money

Ever since I was a little kid, when somebody would ask me "What's your favorite color, honey?" I would always smile and say
"GREEN".
"Oh" they'd say, "like the color of the grass and the leaves on the trees?"
"NO!" I'd answer back. "Like the color of money!"
I don't know what it is, but ever since I can remember, there's just nothing that makes me happier than a crisp dollar bill.
You know how some parents hand their baby a stuffed animal or a doll to keep them quiet? Well, my mom always gave me her change purse to play with and my dad always handed me his money clip so I could count the bills for fun,
And now that I'm older, I got to decorate my own room, so I asked for green wallpaper, green sheets, and a gigantic glass piggy bank.
What can I say? I love the color of money.

My Dream Car

Let me introduce you to my dream car.
This baby is a beautiful baby blue Porsche.
See how shiny and clean it is?
It's brand spanking new.
Right out of the showroom.
Let's take a look inside.
(pantomimes opening the door)
The interior is black leather.
(Takes a big whiff)
I just love that new car smell, don't you?
(Runs her hand over the seat)
That leather! It's so soft, so supple, so smooth!
(Takes keys out of her pocket and gets in and takes a seat)
Let's see if we can start this baby up.
(Puts the key in, starts the car, and smiles)
Listen to this baby purr!
Oh, yeah. This is the most beautiful car in the world.
(Runs her hands over the steering wheel)
It's my dream car, alright.
(Turns off the ignition, gets out and shuts the door.)
I'd love to take you for a spin, but I don't want to waste the gas.
Hey, gas is expensive these days, and..
I'm on an allowance, you know.

A Day at the Beach

(Runs across the hot sand and throws a towel on the ground to step on)
Ay Carrrumba! That sand is hot!!!
(Takes a seat on the towel and looks at the sky and the ocean)
What a beeeautiful day!
(Takes sunscreen out of her bag and starts to lather it on)
I'd better load up on the sunscreen on a day like today.
Or, I'll be burnt to a crisp, like a french fry.
(Finishes lathering and lays back on the towel trying to get comfortable)
(Jumps up suddenly)
Hey, what are you doing?!
You just kicked sand ALL OVER ME!
(Takes a good look at the guy – and he's kind of cute)
Oh, well, That's okay.
I'm sure you didn't mean it.
(Smiles and lays back down)
(Touches her forehead and sits back up again looking at her hand)
EWWWW! (Looks up to the sky)
That bird just.....
EWWWWW!
(Wipes her hand on the towel)
(Leans down and wipes her forehead on the towel too)
Yuck! How gross!
(Gets up and turns her towel over and sits back down.)
(Looking just a little less pleased with it all than when she got here)

A Day at the Beach continued...

(Hears her cell phone ring and gets it out of the bag.)
Hello.
Oh, hey girl, how ya doin?
I'm at the beach.
Ohhh, it's perfect here!!
Uh, huh, don't you wish you were me!
(Conversation fades out as the lights go down.)

You Can Bet Your Dog, It's a Monologue.

Ever since the beginning of time,
It seems that man has known how to rhyme.

For me, ever since the day I could speak
There was only one thing that would come out of my beak.

Everything I said had to Rhyme
Even if you asked me to tell the time.

So, although I want a part in your show
There is something that you really must know.

Any part that you give me to memorize
I may desire or even idolize,

But whatever I read or commit to my brain
Will turn into a rhyme if my brain I must sprain,

And though it may seem like this audition's agog
You can bet your dog, it's a monologue!

Thursday's Child

I was born on a Thursday.
That makes me Thursday's child.
And Thursday's child has far to go.
Remember that children's poem?
Monday's child is fair of face.
Tuesday's child is full of grace.
Wednesday's child is full of woe.
Thursday's child has far to go.
Friday's child is loving and giving.
Etcetera, etcetera.
Well, anyway, I'm Thursday's child and I've got far to go.
What does that mean?
I think it means I'll travel a lot.
I hope so. I want to go as far as I can around the world.
I'm glad I wasn't born on a Saturday.
Saturday's child works hard for a living.
I really don't want to work too hard.
I just want to see the world.

The Seven Natural Wonders of the World

I have a list of places that I want to see in my lifetime.
It starts with the Seven Natural Wonders of the World.
Do you know what they are?
There is the Grand Canyon in Arizona
Victoria Falls in Africa
The Great Barrier Reef in Australia
Mount Everest
Paricutin Volcano
The Northern Lights and
The Harbor of Rio De Janero
Gosh, I hope I get to start on my travels soon!
I've been gathering travel brochures and researching on the internet.
I figure if I manage to go to one natural wonder a year that would be seven years.
Well, that's pretty easy to figure out.
And, if I don't get started until I'm out of college...well, let's see, I'll probably graduate when I'm 22.
That was how old my brother Tom was when he graduated from Harvard.
If I start at 22 and I travel to one natural wonder of the world a year, I'll only be 29 when I've reached my goal.
Then, when I'm 30, I'll settle down, have a family, etc.
Do you think I'm planning too far ahead?

Snowflakes

They say that there aren't two snowflakes alike.
Hard to believe isn't it?
They look so much alike, but you really couldn't find two identical snowflakes if you searched far and wide for thousands of years.
It's the same with people.
There are no two people in this world who are exactly alike.
I ought to know because I'm an "identical twin".
My sister Theresa and I look exactly alike.
To most people that is.
But we know our differences as much as we know our similarities.
Not just in our appearance, but also in our personalities.
For instance, I'm actually about one quarter of an inch taller than Theresa. She wears a size 7 shoe and I wear a 6 and a half.
My favorite food is pizza, but Theresa is the only person I've ever met who actually can't stand the stuff.
We're both pretty neat, but Theresa is absolutely a neat freak.
It's kind of hard because we share a room and she just can't stand it when I forget to make my bed.
I guess, the truth of the matter is, we're really not identical twins.
We're snowflake sisters.

Sisters

Sisters are a wonderful gift. I have three sisters and we are sooo much more than sisters. We are the best of friends.
I am the youngest, so I'm the baby of the family.
My oldest sister is 19 and her name is Carol.
Cindy is 16. Brooke is 14.
And I'm twelve.
I think a lot of my friends envy me because I get sooo much love and attention from my sisters. I never have to be lonely because there is usually always someone there for me.
When I need advice, there is always someone to ask.
And because they're all older than me, they've been through just about everything that I'm going through or about to go through.
I hope we always stay close.
When I think about Carol going to college this year, it's kind of hard.
But, we've promised each other that no matter how far apart we are geographically, we will always be in each other's hearts.
And, no matter what problems lie ahead for each of us, we will always be there for each other.
That's what sisters are for.

Brothers

My name is Carolyn Tabitha Turnberry and I am the youngest child in a family of seven.
What's even more interesting than that is that I am the only girl.
That's right, I have six brothers.
Steven, Larry, Kerry, Richard, David, and Sam.
I'm not bragging, but I think I have the best brothers in the world.
Steven is like a math genius and whenever I have a problem with something in math, I go to him.
Larry is the hilarious one.
If you ever need to laugh, Larry is the one who can get you rolling on the floor. He'll make you laugh so hard that your side hurts.
Kerry is quiet and shy, but you can go to him with all of your secrets. He'll never break a promise.
Richard, David and Sam are triplets, but they are nothing alike.
They look EXACTLY alike though and they are constantly playing tricks on our family; so they really keep us guessing.
And me? I'm pretty special, I guess. Cause I'm the only girl.
So, they spoil me. It's true. But, I'm not complaining.
Having six brothers? It's incredible.
Being the only girl? Priceless.

Confessions of a Couch Potato

I confess.
I'm a couch potato.
In fact, when you look up couch potato in the dictionary, you probably see a picture of me there.
I love doing all of the things that a couch potato does.
TV watching of course is number one.
But that's a no brainer.
But you probably wouldn't guess that I can make a peanut butter and jelly sandwich while sitting on the couch.
Do all of my homework, while watching TV of course.
Clip my toenails.
Give myself a manicure.
Email my friends on my wireless laptop.
Surf the web.
Play video games.
Read comic books.
And answer the phone.
All without ever getting off the couch.
I've timed myself, and one day I stayed on the couch for five hours straight after getting home from school.
That's my record actually.
Five hours!
Then I just rolled off the couch and crawled into bed.
Yeah, I know, not everybody takes pride in their couch potato status, but then again, hey, I am what I am.

City Girl

My name is Annabel Maria Jones and I live on a great big farm in Oklahoma.
But I'm really a city girl at heart.
I know that I'm a city girl, cause my Drama teacher took us on a field trip last year to New York City.
The Big Apple.
It was amazing.
It was the first and only time I've been there and I LOVED IT.
I did not even want to go home.
We saw the Empire State building, the Statue of Liberty, and two Broadway Shows.
I just totally fell in love.
And, ever since that trip I have known exactly what I wanna do when I grow up.
I want to be a Broadway star with an apartment right in Manhattan.
I wanna be a City Girl.

Fast Forward

Wouldn't it be great if life were like a DVD and you controlled the remote?
Imagine yourself sitting in math class taking a test.
All of these problems don't look familiar!
OH MY GOSH! You studied the wrong thing.
Just get out the remote, and hit Rewind.
Go all the way back to last night and VOILA,
you can find the right chapter and when you're done, just fast forward yourself right back into class.
It would also come in handy for those times you'd just like to pass super quickly.
Like that hour you spend in the dentist's chair every so often.
Or, the lecture dad's always giving you for forgetting to take out the garbage.
And, there would always be those times that you just want to go back to and relive every now and then.
I wouldn't mind rewinding all the way back to my fifth birthday when Aunt Sally gave me a puppy.
Or the trip that we took when we went to see my sister graduate from college. Wouldn't that be fun?
I guess the only bad part would be if you lost your remote.
I know a few people who think I talk too much.
Some of my teachers for instance.
If they got control of my remote, well, I think we all know what button they'd push.
PAUSE!
(Freezes for a moment)
(Then, blackout)

How to Be an Expert on Any Subject

My Aunt is a motivational speaker who travels around the world teaching people how to make more out of their lives.
One week I was out of school for some reason and she took me with her on one of her short trips to give a little talk.
I thought it was going to be super boring, but it was actually kind of cool.
We went to this big fancy company in Philadelphia and she talked to a group of employees about how to improve their lives.
She showed them how to organize and how to plan and how to set goals for themselves.
She told them that they could become an expert on any subject just by reading five books on that subject.
Five books!
That doesn't seem like such a huge thing.
On the flight home I thought a lot about that.
I usually read fiction because I love a good story, but I sure wouldn't mind feeling like an expert on something.
She claimed it would boost your self-esteem.
So, now, I'm trying to decide where to start.
What do I really want to know a lot about?
Acting?
Fly Fishing?
Astronomy?
The possibilities are just endless.

Lost and Found

My friend Lisa came over yesterday.
We had such a great time.
She just moved to our town a few months ago and we hit it off right away.
We met in school of course, but as it turns out she and her mom only live about two blocks away.
I never asked her where her dad is.
But yesterday, we sat around at my house writing letters to our pen pals.
I write to a girl in Russia and she writes to one in England.
Our geography teacher helped us find pen pals as part of this big project called One World.
Well, after Lisa went home, I realized that her letters were still on my desk.
And as I picked one up, I noticed it was addressed to her dad.
I should have put it down right then, but....
I didn't.
It was all about how she missed him and she wished and hoped he would come home soon and patch things up with her mom.
How she hoped it all really wasn't her fault.
I've got to give her that letter when I see her in school tomorrow.
I guess I'll just pretend that I didn't read it.
What would you do?

The Invisible Girl

Sometimes I feel like I'm the invisible girl.
Everybody around me gets noticed for something.
They're sooo smart, or they're soooo pretty,
Or they're sooo funny.
They're always soooo SOMETHING.
Me? I'm just sooooo ME.
Soooo average.
Soooo boring.
Soooo totally invisible.
Sometimes people walk by me in the hall at school and it's really like I'm not there at all.
I know, it's probably my own fault.
I don't try to stand out.
I don't make an effort.
I don't apply myself.
But I don't care.
I guess.
Sometimes it's not so bad being the invisible girl.
Going unnoticed sort of lets you be a fly on the wall, you know.
You'd be surprised at the secret conversations that you can overhear and the interesting situations I've been witness to.
Hmmmm. Maybe I'm sooooo sneaky.

Blah, Blah, Blah

My cousin Marybeth is a terrible listener.
I didn't realize that for a while.
I used to go over to her house and tell her my deepest feelings and dreams and she always said the right thing.
Like, "how wonderful", or "how marvelous", or "gee, that's so nice."
Then, I got to thinking about it one day, and I realized that Marybeth always says the same thing. She always has that nice face like she's really interested, but I suddenly wasn't really so sure that she was.
So, I tried an experiment.
I went over and started spilling my guts like I usually do, but every so often, instead of saying real words, I just said a couple of Blah, Blah, Blahs.
And you know what? She said, "gee whiz, that's marvelous!"

How Romantic

SO DO YOU LIKE ME OR NOT?
What do you mean, “I’m too aggressive?”
Yeah, when I want something, I go after it.
So, is that supposed to be a bad thing?
Believe me buster, I am the best thing that’s ever happened to you.
I’m not like those other girls who try to act real demure and bat their eyelashes. I am straightforward and frank.
NO, MY NAME ISN’T FRANK.
It’s Matilda, silly.
I mean I tell it like it is.
And the way it is, is that I am your new girl friend.
Whether you like it or not!
Cause I think you are just too cute for words.
So Steven honey, this is your lucky day.
And don’t worry if you’re not sold on me yet.
I tend to grow on people.

Don't Walk in My Head with Your Dirty Feet

There's an old Native American proverb that goes, "Don't walk in my head with your dirty feet."
Do you know what that means?
I didn't think so.
You see, what it means is, don't go trying to put your negative or hateful thoughts in my mind.
I like to keep my mind focused on the positive.
I like to try to stay upbeat.
And I'm getting a little tired of having to constantly tune out your negativity.
I'm usually able to tune it out, but I have to admit, lately, you're really starting to get to me.
Believe me, if I wanted to sit around and whine, I could probably think of a million things to complain about.
But I choose not to.
And I don't need to start every day by hearing you whine and complain.
It's starting to rub off.
And what starts out to be a good day, suddenly turns sour.
So, please, please, please, either wash your feet, or don't walk in my head!!

The Best Recipe I Never Made

I once entered a cooking contest with a recipe that I never made.
And I won!
It was hilarious.
I just made up the recipe based on my favorite ingredients and a lot of imagination.
But, I really never thought I'd win.
I entered one night on the internet when I couldn't sleep.
And about a month later, I got a call.
"Congratulations, you are the first place winner in our Dessert Bake Off."
I could have fainted.
I never dreamed that my concoction of bananas, chocolate chips, pistachios, buttered pecans, strawberry flavored marshmallows, caramel syrup, fudge sauce, tapioca, rice pudding and sugar cookie dough could taste so good.

The Secret at the Top of the Stairs

There's a secret at the top of the stairs, under the wooden plank that always goes "EEE" when you step on it.
It's a treasure map and it's been there for about a hundred years.
Of course, you're probably wondering why it's still there.
Why we haven't used it to go and claim the buried treasure.
Well, that's kind of part of the secret too.
(looks around to make sure that no one is listening)
You see, the treasure is cursed. And it would be very, very, unlucky for the person who removes the treasure map from the staircase.
Very unlucky my friends.
So, even though I'm tempted every time I hear that creak under my feet, I could never be tempted enough.
But, what I am going to do, is find a way to remove the curse.
And then, the treasure will be mine.

Give or Take a Few

I have done about 4 million, three thousand dishes in my lifetime. Give or take a few. You see, lucky me, when the chores were handed out in my family, I was given the kitchen cleanup. And boy does that kitchen get dirty. Especially the dishes. I have been trying to lobby my parents for paper plates, but they are really into the environment, so that won't fly. Hey, I'm into the environment too, but if you had to do the dishes every single night of your life, I think you'd see my point of view.

There are times when I think I can't face another dirty dish, another crusty fork, or a slimy spoon.

But, I just talk to myself and somehow I pull through.

I am saving my allowance money for something special though. No, it isn't jewelry or clothes. I am going to buy a dishwasher!

The Last Straw

This is the last straw! You have interrupted me when I'm on the phone for the last time. I am going to put a sign on my bedroom door that says KEEP OUT, AND THAT MEANS YOU!
Oh, go ahead and tell mom. I don't care! I'll tell on you too! How you're always coming in here without asking, borrowing my stuff and not putting it back.
Leaving your toys on the floor where they could trip me and break my neck. What do you think she'll say about that?
(Ugggh)
Don't start crying.
I...
It's okay. I'm..
I'm just mad, that's all.
I'm not gonna put up a sign.
I just wish you would knock that's all.
I mean, sometimes I'm having a private conversation.
Of course you're special to me.
Yes, more special than anybody.
I know, I love you too.
(Ughhhh)
Why can't I ever stay mad at you?

And the Winner Is...

(gushing and breathless) Well, thank you, thank you so much.
This is such an honor, receiving this award today.
And, I am totally in awe of all of the other actresses that lost.
I mean, you are all so great. I can't believe how great it feels to know that I'm that much better than you!
And, I would like to thank all of the little people who have helped me along the way: my agent, my hairdresser, the girl who does my nails. Oh, and the way cute guy at the donut shop who always gives me my mocha latte just the way I like it. Two sugars and no whipped cream! (giggles)
This is just such an amazing honor, and I hope I'm not leaving anyone out.
Oh yeah, the other actors in the play were sooo helpful.
I mean, without you, I would have been the only one on stage.
And then, I guess, it wouldn't even be a play.
It would be a monologue.
Which would still be really great of course, but it's just so much more interesting as a play. And, well, to our director who cast me.
Harry Steinfeld, you are a genius!!
Thank you. I love you all!

Closed for the Day

I'm sorry, but this is supposed to be a team project guys.
And everyday you keep coming to me for the ideas.
I'm not an idea factory you know.
I mean, in a way, I'm flattered, but on the other hand, I am not supposed to be doing all the work.
You know, if we really tried to sit around a table and brainstorm, you all could probably come up with something that you would like just as much as what I would come up with.
There is more than one solution to any problem.
But, (sighs) as long as I keep giving in and doing all the work, coming up with ideas, etcetera, you won't bother. It's just too easy to sit back and relax and do nothing. And when we get our grade, it will be OUR grade, and I just don't think that's fair. So, I'm putting up a sign on the idea factory folks. CLOSED FOR THE DAY. I've done my part!
Now, guess what? It's your turn.

But Uh...

Do you have any friends that you just love, but they talk so much and so fast that you can never get a word in edgewise? You know, you've been talking to them for a least an hour on the phone and suddenly you realize that your only contribution to the conversation has been a series of futile attempts to interrupt?

Like, she says "When we go to the beach on Saturday, you can bring your camera." And you say, "But uh" and she's off and running again. You'll end up bringing your camera whether you wanted to or not, cause she'll never give you five seconds to say you can't or you'd rather not, or whatever. And she'll have changed the subject so many times by the end of the conversation that your head will be in a spin. And all you can do when she suddenly says, "Oh hey, my mom's home, gotta go" is say B...

The Apology

(knocks on door and unhappily waits for it to be answered)
(Not very friendly) Hi.
(squirms a bit and looks mostly at her feet at first)
I'm here to apologize.
I'm sorry for...talking about you behind your back.
It was wrong and mean, and I don't know...what I was thinking.
Cause, it was just really stupid.
So, I'm sorry.
And, I hope that you can....forgive me and that we ....
Can be friends again.
Someday.
I mean, I know I hurt your feelings and you probably won't trust me again for a long time, but I want you to know that you can trust me. I won't ever, ever do what I did again.
I've really learned my lesson.
Cause, your friendship meant a lot to me.
That's all.

La di da, la di da

There's this girl in my neighborhood who always starts the latest trend, like whatever sneakers are going to be popular, or whatever game we all start playing in the summer and can't seem to stop. But the coolest thing that I really envy is that every summer she starts saying something that catches on until everybody's saying it. Last year she started saying, "la di da, la di da" all the time. And sure enough, before long, all the girls were going around saying, "la di da, la di da". That's so cool. I mean, I wish I could do that. And I have tried, I really have. Like last summer, I started saying "Oy" after just about every sentence. But it didn't catch on. People just looked at me like I was from another planet. So, I finally just gave in and said, "la di da, la di da."

On the Side

I'd like to order a large lemonade with two slices of lime, please.
Is the lemonade made with fresh-squeezed lemons?
Because if it isn't fresh squeezed, I'll have an iced tea.
Oh, okay then, iced tea will be fine. Do you have raspberry tea, because that's my favorite? Oh. Well, I guess regular tea will be fine. But, I'll need lots of ice and I'd like it on the side. And I'd like a slice of lime, but also a slice of lemon. You do have lemons don't you? Yes, well you'd think you'd have fresh squeezed lemonade then, but anyway I'm ready to order my meal, if I may.
I'd like to order the pulled pork sandwich, but I don't want it on a bun, can I get it on rye? Wonderful. And I'd like the barbeque sauce, but I'd like it on the side and I'd like an extra bit of barbecue sauce please, because I won't like it if the pork is dry.
And it comes with? Oh, french fries? You don't have coleslaw?
Well, then in that case scratch the pulled pork sandwich and give me a burger well done. And please don't bring me the tea, a glass of water will be fine. Yes, that's right, the ice on the side.

Quince

When I'm fifteen years old my parents will throw me a party. We call it Quince in Spanish, which just means 15. It's like the American custom of celebrating a girl's sweet sixteen. We're going to buy a beautiful gown and I'm going to put my hair up. My sister Maria will help me put on make up and I'm going to have a professional photo session at Viscaya. It's a beautiful mansion in Miami. All of my cousins had their Quince photo session there. I'm really excited. But I'm most excited about the party. There will be a live band and dancing. I got to help select the menu. We made an appointment with the caterers and I sat with my parents and helped make the decisions, like an adult. It's a very special time in a Cuban-American girl's life, Quince. And I know it's as special for my parents as it is for me. Their little girl, their baby, is growing up and becoming a woman.

The Ballet

The other night I went to the ballet with my Aunt and afterwards I just kept wishing that I could do something so beautiful. The ballerinas were so perfect. I just couldn't stop thinking of how they have so much to give to the world. I guess you could say I felt kind of miserable, because I wanted to know what it would be like to have such a purpose in life.
I was feeling jealous, I guess.
That night when I went to sleep I dreamed that I was a teacher in a school for the blind, helping blind children learn to play the piano. I was literally sitting at a piano with a little boy who couldn't see and I was teaching him to learn to play. It was such a realistic dream and when I woke up, I just lay there thinking about it for a really long time. I felt like it was a sign.
I felt like my dream was telling me that maybe teaching is the beautiful thing that I am meant to do in this world.
It was like my dream was saying, some of the most beautiful and purposeful lives are not on stage for the world to see.

EUGOLONOM

Did you know that *stressed* spelled backwards is *desserts*?
No, I'm not trying to tell you to eat Chocolate Cake to get rid of your stress. I just have a fascination with backwards words.
You could say it's kind of a hobby of mine, I guess.
I collect words that are interesting when spelled backwards.
I call them BackWords. Get it? BackWords.
B -A -C-K-W-O-R-D-S
Oh hey, do you know what they call a word that is spelled the same backwards and forwards?
Like the name Bob?
Bob, B – O – B.
Can you tell me if I just spelled it backwards, or forwards?
If you can guess, you win the prize behind door number 3.
No, but seriously, do you know what they call a word that is spelled the same backwards and forwards?
Well, neither do I! Go look it up if you want to know.
Anyway, my favorite word spelled backwards is actually my name, Mary.
Mary spelled backwards is Yram.
Isn't that cool?
Yram.
Another good word spelled backwards is hamburger.
I like to ask my mom if we're having regrubmah for dinner again.
She usually just ignores me, or rolls or her eyes, but I get a huge kick out of it. What's really great is when she says "Enough!"
Enough sounds just like "funny" backwards,

(continued)

so, when she's really annoyed and she says "enough,"
that just kills me.
My friend Lynnette is sort of into BackWords too.
Sometimes when she comes over, we try to communicate
using only BackWords. But that's pretty hard.
I mean, really, can you say "Let's go to the pool" backwards?
It's not easy.

21 Days

Did you know that it takes 21 days to form a habit?
Well, I'm trying to change the way I laugh in 21 days.
Yeah, the way I laugh.
It's really just kind of a habit, the way a person laughs.
It's like somewhere along the way they started laughing a certain way and after 21 days they were set.
I mean, you know how some people snort, (example) or some people sort of wheez (example)?
Do you think they have to laugh that way?
I think it's just a habit.
So, right now I'm in the process of selecting my new laugh.
This is really the most important part of the process, because I don't want to choose a new laugh and then 21 days later, realize that I hate it.
Then I'll have to start all over from scratch.

The Man I Marry

(sitting around talking at a slumber party)
First of all, let me just say that I'm not getting married until I'm 25, at least.
(a little bit louder toward the door)
So, mom if you're hearing this don't freak out.
Okay, let's see, the man I marry...
Well, he'll have to be strong.
Like my dad.
And have a good job.
Like my mom. (giggles)
He'll have to love both of my parents just as much as I do, or I absolutely will not marry him.
No matter what.
He'll have to love children because I want to have 7.
Well, some of them will be adopted of course.
He'll have to love skiing as much as I do.
And animals.
And my pets will have to love him.
That's the most important thing of all.
If my dogs don't like a guy....he's toast.
And that is the guy that I plan to marry.
Okay, your turn.

Sugared and Spiced

What are little girls made of?
Sugar and spice and everything nice.
That's what little girls are made of.
I wonder who wrote that.
Do you know?
It's kind of nice actually.
I mean sometimes I'm sweet like sugar, and other times I'm a little spicy. And everything nice? Well, I try.
What are little boys made of?
Hmmm. That one's always harder for me to remember.
Something like snails and pails and puppy dog tails.
Right?
That doesn't make as much sense, does it?
Puppy dog tails? That's pretty cool.
I guess.
But, Sugar and Spice.
And everything nice.
Now, that's what little girls are made of!

The True Test

Do you know the difference between truth and integrity? Truth is what you do or say in honesty when someone is watching or listening. Integrity is what you do or say when no one is watching or listening. That's what my yoga teacher told us.

I thought about that a lot yesterday morning. I went to school early to help Mrs. Hall grade papers for her sixth grade American History class. I'm her aide once a week in the mornings and I also have her for Civics class second period. Well, yesterday, in second period we were supposed to be having this really important essay test. Mrs. Hall had been telling us about it for a week. Three essay questions, she kept saying, on the last three chapters we've read.

So, anyway, to get back to the morning, when I got to Mrs. Hall's room to help her grade papers, she said she had to leave the room for a minute or two.

So here I am sitting at her desk grading papers when my red pen ran out of ink.

So, I opened the drawer to get one and there staring me right in the face was a folder with *7th Grade Essay Test* written on it.

If Mrs. Hall ever caught me doing something like that... She'd never trust me again.

So, I got up and looked through the blinds to see if she was nearby.

I could see her.

She was way out in the parking lot with Miss Harris.

They were unloading a bunch of boxes from her car.

The True Test (continued)

I knew I had plenty of time, so I went back over to the desk and opened the drawer.
But, then, I thought about what my yoga teacher had said.
And I thought, is it really worth it?
To sacrifice my integrity just so I'll get a good grade?
And just because Mrs. Hall doesn't see me, won't I feel just as rotten if I see myself?
There were two tests for me yesterday in Mrs. Hall's class.
And as it turns out...I passed them both.

How Not to Mingle

Hey Angela, I really appreciate you coming out to this party with me while you're in town.
Don't worry about not knowing anybody.
Just stick with me, as soon as he answers the door, I'll turn on the Party Charm.
THE PARTY CHARM.
Remember?
That's the thing I invented to help people overcome their fear of parties. You know, how to make conversation, what to do if you don't know anybody.
That sort of thing.
Okay, here we go.
(Knocks on the door.)
Stick with me and you'll see The Party Charm at work.
(The door opens)
Hey Charlie, what's happening?
This is my friend Angela.
Yo, Yo, Yo everybody.
Angela's in the house.
Give her your love.
(Starts to dance while talking)
Hey, great music Charlie! Very different, but very cool.
(spins around and dances over to someone else)
Whassup J.J?
Nice crib.
(motions to Angela to follow her)
(Dances over to someone else)
Hey, whoooo are yooooou?

How Not to Mingle (continued)

This is Angela and I'm April.
APRRRILL and ANGELA
Yeah!! That's right.
(Dances back to Charlie)
Hey, Charlie, I have one question for you?
Why isn't anybody dancing, but me?
What kind of party is this anyhow?
What's a wake?

Understudy

Why am I always the understudy? Mrs. Hotchkin that's not true. I am not the best understudy you've ever had. I mean, maybe it is true, but who wants to the best understudy. Always wishing and hoping that someone gets sick or accidentally breaks a leg? What kind of life is that for me? Mrs. Hotchkin you just have to give me a role, a real role, in the spring play this year. I don't care what it is. I'll play a doorman, I'll play a tree, I'll be an ice-cream cone. I'll be a shoe. But Mrs. Hotchkin, I refuse, I will not, I can not understudy any more. WHAT? You want me to audition for Eliza Doolittle? The lead in My Fair Lady? Oh my gosh!! That's such a huge role. Mrs. Hotchkin, I love you!

Poor Old Mrs. Hatch

In seventh grade Mrs. Hatch made us dress out for gym every day.
No matter what.
Even on the coldest winter days she had no pity.
Walking up to the girls' locker room we always read the sign.
Ms. Hugley's class Don't Dress Out. Meet me in the Gym.
Mrs. Hatch's class Dress Out! Meet me on the track.
It was a good way to get us to run I guess.
We ran just to keep warm I think.
And old Mrs. Hatch would stand out there with the wind blowing through her blue hair. And her whistle stuck between her blue lips.
And she'd blow and blow.
And she'd yell too.
"Smith, go around again. This isn't a promenade."
"Jackson, over here for 30 push ups.
I don't care if it takes you all day."
And then back in the locker room,
"Get in those showers. A little cold water never killed any-body.
A little icy water? Even better. It'll wake up some of you sleep walkers."
We hated Mrs. Hatch.
And we prayed that one day she'd see the light and let us have a break.
Then, one day, a miracle happened.
Walking up to the gym door, I saw the sign.
Ms. Hugley's class Don't Dress Out. Meet me in the gym.

Poor Old Mrs. Hatch
(Continued)

Mrs. Hatch's class Don't Dress Out.
Meet Mrs. Baxter in the gym.
Our substitute teacher met us with a smile.
"Where is Mrs. Hatch?" we all asked.
"Poor Mrs. Hatch slipped on a piece of ice beside the track yesterday after school and she'll be out for a few days."
Poor old Mrs. Hatch.

Shhhh

Shhhhhh! Be quiet, my parents are next door talking about what I'm getting for my birthday.
Shhhh! I'm serious.
(leans in to the wall to hear)
(eyes get wide with excitement)
Oh my Gosh!!!
(jumps up and down)
Oh my gosh, oh my gosh, oh my gosh!!!
I heard them say "car."
No, I swear I did.
Shhhhh.
I can't hear them now.
Okay, here they go again.
(listens intently then frowns)
Oh no, oh no, I...
My dad just said, "No car."
(drops down on the bed)
No car.
(puts her head on the pillow and starts to cry)
(quiets down and listens again)
Wait, I can hear something again.
It sounds like skiing. Ski trip.
Ski trip with friends.
(smiling) I swear, "ski trip with friends!"
Oh my gosh.
(Jumps off the bed and hops up and down and squeals, then covers her mouth)
(listens again)

Shhhh (continued)

(yells loudly) Nothing mom, everything is fine.
(giggles)
(yells again) I love you guys!!!

The Wrong Place at the Wrong Time

Did you ever feel like you were born in the wrong place at the wrong time? I do. All the time. It started when I was a little kid actually. I just always liked old-fashioned things. Antiques, you know.
And I've always loved movies about the past. The clothes that people wore in the olden days and the way they traveled. By horse and buggy and by train.
It's weird and it's kind of annoying because I just can't get into the world today.
It's like I need to be part of a different world that I just can't be a part of.
That's why I love stories about time travel.
I imagine that I'll be walking along one day and suddenly come upon a magical portal that will take me back in time.
I have dreams that I'm in old-time dresses and people are doing old-fashioned things, like reading books out loud together by the lantern and planting their own gardens.
(sighs)
I wish I could be a modern girl, but I can't.
I was just born in the wrong place at the wrong time.

Stage Positions

UR Up Right	URC Up Right of Center	UC Up Center	ULC Up Left of Center	UL Up Left
R Rignt	RC Right of Center	C Up Center	LC Left of Center	L Left
DR Down Right	DRC Down Right of Center	DC Down Center	DLC Down Left of Center	DL Down Left

Apron

Audience

Drama Terms

Ad lib
To make up lines in a monologue or play, on the spur of the moment without any preparation.

Apron
The area of the stage in front of the curtain.

Backstage
Areas of the theater behind the stage.

Blackout
All of the stage lighting goes out and the stage is completely dark.

Book, the
The script. When you are "off book" that means you have memorized your lines.

Breaking the Fourth Wall
Talking directly to the audience.

Business
An actor's physical activities. Particularly those activities that reveal her character during a performance.

Cue
A pre-arranged signal that tells the actor to proceed with an action. A cue may be a word, a sound, a light, or some character's action.

Curtain Call
When the cast comes out on stage to take a bow at the end of a play.

Downstage
The area of the stage that is closest to the audience.

Entrance, an
When the actor walks on stage.

Flat
Scenery that consists of canvas stretched over a wooden frame.

Fourth Wall
The imaginary wall that separates an actor from the audience.

Hold (for Applause or Laughter)
To wait until the applause or laughter dies down to continue with the next line.

Improvisation
To make up a scene or a monologue on the spur of the moment, without any preparation.

Mime
A person who pantomimes.

Monologue
A speech acted out by one actor.

Off-stage
You are off-stage when you are in the wings or backstage.

Pace
An actor's rhythm when acting out a scene.

Pantomime
To act without speaking.

Playwright
A person who writes plays.

Prompt
Reminding an actor of her lines during a performance.

Prompt copy
A copy of a script that has been annotated to include all of the lighting and sound cues as well as the actors' movements.

Proscenium
The frame that sometimes surrounds the opening or front of a stage.

Set
All of the scenery in a play.

Stage Directions
The playwright's directions to the actor.

Strike, to
To remove the set from the stage.

Upstage
The area of the stage that is farthest from the audience.

Wings
The area of the stage that is off to the left or the right, out of the audience's line of sight.

Notes:

Notes:

Notes:

Notes:

Notes:

Notes:

Notes:

Acting Out
On Location
VOL. 1
Vocalization
Monologues
Relaxation
Pantomime
Scenes
Acting Class on DVD
At the Beach!
Acting Lessons for kids!
In the Desert!
Use in class or at home!
DVD

About the Author

Mary Depner taught Drama in South Florida for ten years. She has performed professionally, directed countless productions, and studied Opera. She has a Bachelors degree in Acting and Directing and a Master's Degree, believe it or not, in Information Technology. Currently, she resides in South Florida.

Made in the USA
Lexington, KY
16 May 2012